OSCAR THE O

By Sue Flint
Illustrated by Rosa Brown

Oscar says...

Read books.

**Books will teach you things
you may not learn elsewhere.**

They will thrill and inspire you.

They will make you happy.

Oscar says..........
Read books.
Books will teach you things you may
not learn elsewhere.
They will thrill and inspire you.
They will make you happy.

Oscar says...

Smile.

Do it now.

It makes you feel better and others who see you will be happy too.

Oscar says...

Be kind, even to those who hurt your feelings.

Kindness shows a great strength, a good heart and often stops unhelpful behaviour.

Oscar says ...

If someone tells you "Your hair looks nice" or
"I like your T-shirt or trainers"
Say "thank you" in return.

If someone tells you "Well done" or "That's
clever" or "You tried really hard"
Say "thank you" in return.

These are compliments – they are a gift wrapped
up in words which will make you feel good inside.

Oscar says ......

It doesn't matter what you have or what you wear.

What matters is who you are and what you want to be.

POWER OFF

Oscar says...

**Turn off your television, tablet or I-pad
at least one hour before bedtime to rest your
busy brain.**

**Sleep well, it refreshes and strengthens you for
the next day.**

Oscar says...

Try something new; even if you aren't good at it, you will remember it later.

Oscar says...

**Making mistakes is not a bad thing.
Everyone occasionally does things in a different way
or drops something.**

Saying sorry is helpful and shows a strength of your character.

Mistakes and accidents help us to learn another way of doing things.

Oscar says...

Always have a tissue in your pocket or up your sleeve.
You might need to sneeze or wipe your nose.
It will catch any germs and can be thrown in the bin afterwards.

Or perhaps use it to wipe away tears if you cry.

Oscar says...

Have good manners; use words like please, thank you, excuse me and may I. If you ask for something, always say "Please."

If not, you may be asked "What's the magic word?" or "What do you say?"

"Please" is a good manners word.

Manners are important. If you don't use them people may think you are cheeky and decide not to give you what you want.

Sometimes though, even when we do say "please" the answer can sometimes be "no".

We have to accept we can't always have everything we want.

Oscar says...

It is not fair that your brother, sister or friend has more toys or treats than you do.

Try not to be angry.

It is not fair that it's raining on your birthday or that someone let you down.

Be sad for a little while only.

It is not fair that some people have lots of food, nice homes and happy families, while others do not have much at all.

Be grateful for what you have.

It is not fair that someone you love, or your pet, got sick and died.

Remember the good days you had together.

Life is not always fair; it's just the way things are.

Oscar says.

Sharing is caring.

Play together with others letting them use your bike, ball, game or toys.

They will remember your kindness.

Tell someone how you feel, they will help you through a difficult time.

If you love animals, insects, books or cars share your enthusiasm and knowledge with others.

They might be interested too.

If you have too many teddies or toys ask an adult to give the ones you don't use to charity so that someone else can enjoy them.

SHARING

Oscar says...

You can be wise if you learn these things while you are still young.

You will be wise if you read, share, play, are kind, give and receive compliments, have good manners and know that life has lots of ups and downs.

You will grow up to be clever, sensible and caring; someone who others will want to be like.

Be the best person you can be.

Twit t'wooooo!!

Follow the author on social media -
Facebook: Sue Flint, Author
Twitter: @tweetsue13
Blog: https://sueflintsfs.blogspot.com

APS Books
www.andrewsparke.com

Printed in Great Britain
by Amazon